POPPY AND POLLO GO TO MOUNT OLYMPOS!

The Myth of Persephone

Persephone, the goddess of spring, was a daughter of Zeus, king of the gods, and of Demeter, the goddess of crops and fertility. She was also the goddess of the underworld through her match with Hades, and the heroine of one of the greatest tales of Greek mythology. She will forever be identified with the pomegranate seeds, four in number, which she consumed in the underworld. This act obliged her to remain in Hades' domain for four months of the year, before being allowed to return to her mother in the spring, when the fruits of the earth were happily renewed.

Poppy & Pollo
go to
Mount Olympos!

written and illustrated by

Paul Watkins

FORMAT BOOKS

For Persephone

Published by
Format Books
23 Jeffreys Street
London NW1 9PS
www.formatbooks.com

Text and illustrations © Paul Watkins

A catalogue record for this book is available
from the British Library

ISBN 978-0-903372-16-9

Printed and bound by CPI Group (UK) Ltd, Croydon CR0 4YY

Cover design and illustration by the author

Also in this series
Felipe & Esmeralda go to The Galapagos!

Poppy and Pollo lived on a Greek island,
in an old village surrounded by vineyards
and overlooking the sea.

The Greeks loved to name their children after gods.

ZEUS
King of the Gods

HERA
Queen of the Gods

POSEIDON
King of the Sea

HADES
King of the Underworld

HERMES
God of Travel
Messenger god

DEMETER
Goddess of Crops

HEPHAISTOS
God of Fire

ARTEMIS
Goddess
of the
Hunt

ARES
God of War

ATHENA
Goddess
of Wisdom

APHRODITE
Goddess
of Love

DIONYSOS
God of
Wine

Poppy was a nickname
for **Persephone**, goddess
of spring in ancient Greece.

Pollo was short for
Apollo, god of music
and sunlight.

Poppy's mother **Demeter** worked in the vineyard, tending the rows of grapes. In the autumn Poppy would help her mother with the wine harvest, carrying the baskets of grapes to the press.

Poppy loved to wander over the mountainside, gathering flowers to decorate the house, and herbs and greenery for the cooking pot.

Demeter shared her name with the goddess of crops and cultivation. She had always encouraged Poppy's love of the outdoors and nature. Mother and daughter enjoyed doing things together, not only in the fields but in the kitchen, cooking their favourite recipes.

Poppy's red hair hung in braids, and she often wore flowers in it. Demeter, with her own headdress of golden corn, loved the colour of her daughter's hair, which reminded her of the warm earth of the fields.

Pollo, who lived next door, was a gifted musician and enjoyed playing his *bouzouki*, a special stringed instrument popular in Greece.

His favourite outfit was the uniform of a Greek soldier – an *evzone*.

Pollo lived with his mother **Leto** and twin sister **Artemis**, who was named after the goddess of the hunt. Artemis and Pollo often practised archery together with their bows and arrows.

Poppy was the quietest of the three and spent much of her time on her own, making garlands of flowers for the house.

The three of them had read many stories about their namesakes in a book of Greek myths. They wondered what it would have been like to be a god, with all that divine power!

Their favourite pages showed the names of the family of the gods, with a picture of the king of the gods, Zeus.

In the family tree Zeus was shown with many children, and among them were Persephone, Apollo and Artemis!

The three young people didn't know who their real father was, but whenever Poppy asked her mother Demeter – or when Pollo and Artemis asked their mother Leto – the answer was, 'After you were born, your father, who was a famous mountaineer, ran away to the mountains in northern Greece and I never saw him again.'

So, although they had different mothers they all had the same father, which made Poppy the half-sister of Pollo and Artemis! And just like the mythological deity, their father was called Zeus!

One day Artemis went away to join a special camp for Girl Guides as leader. The Guides would live in the forest and practise woodcraft.

After Artemis left home, Poppy and Pollo spent more time together. They talked about their absent father, and one day Pollo said to Poppy, 'I would like to see our father sometime soon.'

Poppy said, 'Yes, we'll have to go and find him in the mountains. Let's go to Mount Olympos!'

But when they told their mothers about their plan, Demeter and Leto were very unhappy. They did not want their children to meet up with their father. 'Zeus is a bad man, who abandoned both of us, your mothers, when you were babies.

'He thought he could escape from his duties as husband and father by hiding at the top of a mountain!'

Their mothers' refusal to let them search for their father only made Poppy and Pollo more determined to make the journey. First they had to find Mount Olympos on a map of Greece...

MOUNT OLYMPOS

ATHENS

Next day, with their map in hand, they went to the harbour to get some travel information.

They noticed something strange about the man behind the counter of 'Hermes Travel', who had little wings sewn on his cap and shoes.

The symbols of the god of travel.

Yes, his name was **Hermes**!

When Poppy and Pollo told him that they wanted to go to Mount Olympos, Hermes said that they were in luck. He was taking a ferry to Athens the next day and they could go together. From Athens they could then take a train to northern Greece...

Poppy and Pollo told Hermes about their plan to find their father Zeus, and were amazed when Hermes said, 'Zeus is my father too! He has had lots of wives – what are your mothers' names?'

When they told him, Hermes said that his mother was called Maia, and that he must be the half-brother of Poppy and Pollo!

They hugged each other joyfully, then Hermes said, 'Did you know you have a very large family, living in different parts of Greece? I will take you to meet them, and they will help you find your father.'

The next day, without telling their mothers,
Poppy and Pollo set off for the port, where
they met Hermes. He led them onto
a large ferry, the *King of the Sea*.

In charge of the
vessel was Captain
Poseidon, who, like
Hermes, was named
after a Greek god.
As chance
would have
it, he was a
brother of Zeus,
which meant he
was Poppy and
Pollo's uncle!

Once they were under way, Captain Poseidon invited them to his cabin, which was full of trophies from his voyages around the world.

The Captain was a terrible show-off, full of stories of his adventures. He invited them all to join him for lunch at the Captain's Table.

Captain Poseidon was also very bad-tempered. His mood seemed to affect the voyage, which became very shaky, the boat plunging through rough seas and high winds. It was very difficult to eat lunch with all the plates sliding about on the table. Poppy and Pollo didn't feel like their lunch at all, but just as they were about to be sick, Captain Poseidon raised his fork in the air and shouted, 'Enough!' To their amazement, the sea suddenly became calm and they were able to finish their meal.

They finally reached Piraeus, the port of Athens, and took a taxi into the city. The train to the north would not leave until the following day, so Hermes said that Poppy and Pollo could stay with Sister **Athena**.

Sister Athena was very strict. She wore an owl, the symbol of wisdom, as a brooch, and a large hat like a helmet, even indoors. Her house was full of ancient pots and statues. Sister Athena was surprised to learn that she had a new brother and sister!

Next day Sister Athena took Poppy and Pollo to the Acropolis and showed them the monuments built by the ancient Greeks 2250 years ago.

The grandest and most beautiful building was the Parthenon, the special temple of the city's patron goddess, Athena.

Although entry to the building was forbidden, Sister Athena took no notice of the signs and marched into the sacred room at the end of the temple, where she stood proud and erect, like an ancient statue.

The guard was very angry with Sister Athena for going inside the Parthenon and asked them all to leave the Acropolis.

That evening they all met up for dinner. The owner of the taverna, **Dionysos**, brought a large bottle of wine and some grapes to the table. Poppy and Pollo were amazed when Hermes told them Dionysos was their brother!

Dionysos had lots of young friends, who came and sat at the table with them. They had wild hair and tattoos. They behaved very badly, drinking and shouting, but Dionysos loved them.

The next day, Hermes and Athena took Poppy and Pollo to the station to catch the train to the north.

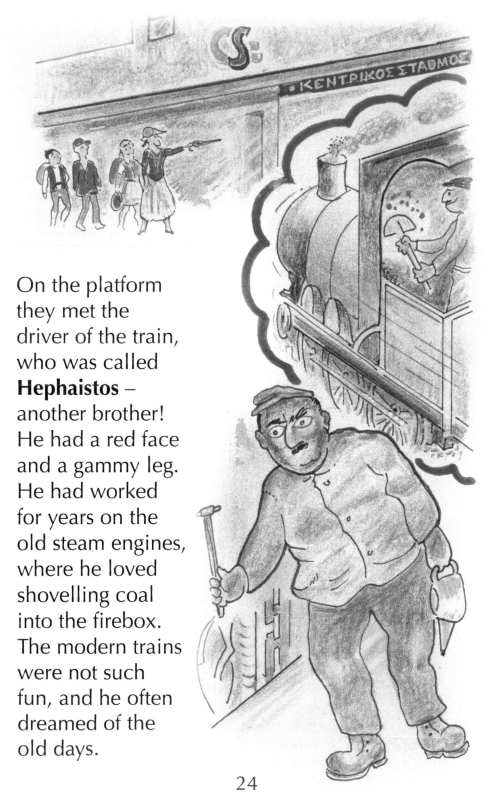

On the platform they met the driver of the train, who was called **Hephaistos** – another brother! He had a red face and a gammy leg. He had worked for years on the old steam engines, where he loved shovelling coal into the firebox. The modern trains were not such fun, and he often dreamed of the old days.

After saying goodbye to Hermes and Sister Athena, Poppy and Pollo began their long journey to the north. Although excited by the thought that they would soon be meeting their father, they remembered that they had not told their mothers where they were going!

Poppy was especially worried about her mother Demeter. 'She must be very anxious to know what has happened to us,' she said.

Neither Demeter nor Pollo's mother Leto knew that the two runaways were already well on their way to the north of Greece!

25

As the train was driven at full speed by Hephaistos, Poppy and Pollo looked down on dizzying views of the coastline, and in the distance, the towering slopes of **Mount Olympos**!

When they arrived at the station for Olympos, Hephaistos said that Poppy and Pollo should meet up with his brother, who was the local military commander. His name was General **Ares** – yet another big brother for Poppy and Pollo!

Hephaistos telephoned General Ares, and a special staff car came to collect them to take them to the army headquarters.

General Ares was pleased to meet Poppy and Pollo, and showed them around the fort. Then he asked them to join him at a military parade.

After the parade, the General invited them to tea and they told him about their search for their father. Ares, who often took his troops into the mountains, said, 'You must ask in the local village.'

Poppy and Pollo thanked General Ares for his help. After their long journey and adventures they thought it would be a nice idea to go to the town and celebrate.

In the town there were lots of tavernas, bars and night clubs. Hermes had given them the addresses of two more of their relatives they could find there. Uncle Hades ran a night club, and Sister Aphrodite a café.

Pollo said he would like to go to the café, which was called 'Aphrodite's Bar'. Poppy said she would rather go to the night club. They agreed to meet up in one hour.

Pollo was amazed by the inside of 'Aphrodite's Bar'. It was decorated with pictures of the ocean and sea creatures. One wall was painted with the scene of the birth of the goddess Aphrodite, being carried ashore on a scallop shell.

The girl who was serving at the tables was like the goddess – Pollo had never seen anyone so beautiful. He ordered lots of drinks, just so she would keep coming to his table. He even played to her on a *bouzouki!*

Meanwhile, Poppy had met an old country woman in the street who was selling dried flowers and herbs in little bags: mint, thyme, oregano and rosemary. She thought it would be nice to take some as a present for her father.

Just then a large gold-painted car pulled
up and a man with a thick beard and a
black hat leaned out of the window.
'Would you like to go to a
really good café with
beautiful ice cream?'
he asked Poppy.

Hearing the words 'ice cream', Poppy forgot all
about the night club! Although her mother had
warned her about talking to strangers, she only
paused for a moment. 'Hop in,' said the man,
and she climbed into the back of the car, which
she had to share with three very ugly dogs.

A moment later, the strange man dropped Poppy at an ice cream parlour called 'Pomegranates'.

Behind the counter sat another odd-looking man. He was very old, with a wispy beard and a boatman's cap. He had a scoop in his hand, ready to serve her.

She was puzzled to find that there was only one variety of ice cream – pomegranate!

The ice cream was flavoured with pomegranate
and there was a pomegranate seed on the top.
It was delicious!

She loved the ice cream so much that she had
three more. But when she was ready to pay
she discovered that she didn't have any money,
and the ice creams were very expensive.

The old man
behind the
counter, whose
name was
Charon, shook
his head.
'You must pay
me the full
amount for
four ice creams,'
he insisted.

Poppy asked if she could go and find her friend, who would lend her some money, but the old man said no. 'I know your sort,' he said, 'You'll walk out and I'll never see you again!'

'Instead you must come with me to the kitchen, where you can work to pay off your debt!'

He led her through to the back, where there was a door with a neon sign saying 'Underworld'. It was her uncle Hades' night club!

Inside the club it was dark and scary, with flashing lights and lots of wild-looking dancers swaying to loud music.

Nervously, Poppy followed the dark figure of Charon to a side door into the kitchen.

Here she was startled to see the man in the black hat who had brought her to the ice cream parlour. When Charon told him about Poppy's debt he pointed to the sink, which was piled with dirty dishes. 'I won't let you off until you've washed everything in that sink,' he said.

There was nothing Poppy could do but obey him. This man, she realised, was her uncle **Hades**! She was too frightened to say anything.

If she worked hard, she hoped that she would be able to earn enough to pay for the ice creams – but there was a problem. Every time she thought she had cleared the sink, more washing-up arrived!

Back in 'Aphrodite's Bar', Pollo was still enjoying himself. When the girl came with more drinks he took a deep breath and said, 'My name is Pollo – I'd like to get to know you. What's your name?'

She answered, 'It's **Aphrodite**, and I'm sorry, but I already have a boyfriend, Adonis.'

Then Pollo said, 'Well, I can still hug you, because you're my half-sister!'

Aphrodite was amazed at this news, and threw her arms around Pollo!

Just then, Pollo remembered his plan to meet up with Poppy. He had to say goodbye to Aphrodite. 'We'll meet again soon, I hope!'

He couldn't find Poppy anywhere, so went in search of their uncle Hades' night club. He thought he would ask at the ice cream parlour, 'Pomegranates'. Perhaps Poppy had been there, knowing how much she loved ice cream?

But the old man at the counter shook his head. 'Don't remember her. Don't remember her at all. And there's no night club around here!'

Pollo thought he should call Poppy's mother straight away and tell her what had happened.

Demeter was very relieved to hear from Pollo. 'Where are you? You've been gone for days, and we've been looking everywhere for you!'

Pollo told her about their adventures, and how they were now in the north of Greece on the way to Mount Olympos to find their father.

Demeter cried, 'You're crazy, you'll never find him! And where is Poppy?'

When Pollo told her that Poppy was missing, Demeter gave a loud cry. 'My daughter, my daughter, I must come and find my daughter!'

But Pollo could not wait for Demeter. He decided to ask General Ares for help instead.

Back at the barracks, Ares listened to Pollo's story. Then he said, 'I will call Hades now, and find out if he knows what has happened to Poppy.'

But when he called Hades, there was no reply...

Then Ares said to Pollo, 'There is only one person who might know where Hades has taken Poppy. That is my father Zeus, who is Hades' brother!'

Ares told Pollo that Zeus was a mountaineer who looked after the climbers on Mount Olympos. It would not be easy to find him.

Pollo's answer was simple, 'With your permission, sir, I will go to Mount Olympos!'

Straightaway, Pollo set off for Mount Olympos. In the mountain village he bought some climbing equipment at 'Zeus Mountain Supplies'.

There was a large lady behind the counter who acted very superior, as though Mount Olympos belonged to her.

Nervously, Pollo asked her if she knew where he could find the owner of the store.

'Zeus?' she exclaimed, 'I'm **Hera** and he's my husband, and you'll find him if you're lucky at the top of the mountain!'

Pollo told Hera that he was the son of one of Zeus' previous wives, Leto.

Hera looked very sour. 'I don't want to know about her, or any of his other women,' she said. 'So you must be my stepson or something?'

'Yes,' said Pollo, 'and I'd like to meet my father.'

Hera thought for a moment, then said, 'All right, but you'll have to get a move on. Tonight he should be at the High Refuge.'

Pollo set off immediately. After a couple of hours he started a steep climb up a goat track, which twisted its way through the pine-covered slopes to the treeline below the summit.

When he was about half-way up the mountain he began to feel tired, and at a narrow place where the track edged along a cliff he lost his footing!

He hurtled downwards
into a ravine and was
only saved by the
branches of a pine tree.
But it was a very tall tree
and he could not
climb down.
He shouted for help.

He didn't expect
anyone to be near,
so high up the
mountain, but to
his surprise he
heard a voice
calling out to him.

Looking down,
he saw a group
of Girl Guides
gathered at the
foot of the tree.
By a lucky chance,
he had almost
landed on their
campsite!

He was even more surprised to see that their leader was his twin sister, Artemis, who was looking after the group at their summer camp!

She had a great idea to rescue him. She had her bow and arrow with her, and fixing a length of rope to an arrow, she fired it into the tree. Pollo caught the rope, tied it round a branch and lowered himself to the ground.

It was a wonderful reunion for them.
Like Pollo, Artemis was anxious to find their
father, with the help of her Girl Guide troop.

Pollo told her that they might find Zeus at
the High Refuge. They checked it on a map,
and Artemis said she would follow him
with the Guides.

Pollo continued up the mountain. Some way
along the track he met a large herd of goats,
which ran away at his approach.

Then he was startled to see some wild-looking
goatherds coming out of the trees. They were
very angry that he had frightened their goats and
started chasing him along the track.

Pollo was very frightened, and it took all of his breath and the strength of his legs to stay ahead of them. Just when it seemed they would catch up with him, there was a terrible crash as a big boulder thudded into the ground a few feet away from him. Then another landed close by, and another. They were like thunderbolts! The goatherds ran away, screaming in terror.

Finally escaping the goatherds – and the avalanche – Pollo reached a sign to the High Refuge. Above him he saw a huge bearded man gripping a pole, which he'd used to send some boulders crashing down the mountainside...

'That'll take care of those wretched goats,' the man said in a large booming voice. He looked suspiciously at Pollo. 'Who are you?'

Pollo took a deep breath. 'Your son,' he said.

It was **Zeus**! He looked very scary.
'What's your mother's name?' he boomed.

'Leto,' answered Pollo. Zeus looked puzzled
and scratched his head. Finally he said,
'Ah yes, Apollo! I'm pleased to meet you.'

They shook hands. This was a great event,
and Pollo hoped that Zeus was pleased
to discover his long-lost son.

Zeus was in for another surprise when Artemis arrived with her troop of Girl Guides. When Pollo introduced him to Artemis, he could not believe that she was his daughter, Pollo's twin sister!

At that moment, there was a tremendous whirring sound above them, and looking up, they saw a helicopter hovering overhead with the name 'Hermes Travel' on the side.

The helicopter descended and landed nearby.
Zeus was just as amazed as Pollo when two
figures emerged: Demeter and Hermes!

Demeter ran to give Pollo and Artemis a hug, and
then threw her arms in the air at the sight of Zeus.
'Zeus, you must help me!' she cried. 'Hades has
taken little Poppy, our daughter Persephone.'

'That's not good,' said Zeus. 'My brother is
misbehaving again. We must rescue Persephone.'

Going into the hut he picked up a telephone and dialled a number. A loud voice at the other end, which they all could hear, replied, "Underworld'?'

It was the night club where Poppy had vanished. Zeus was very angry with his brother. 'You're keeping my daughter against her wishes,' he said.

'No I'm not,' said the voice. 'She's happy to be with me. I am her uncle, after all.'

'You must come to Olympos and bring her with you,' Zeus commanded. 'Her mother is here, and she's very anxious and upset.'

'All right,' answered the voice, 'but you'll see for yourself.'

Zeus sent Hermes to the town in his helicopter to pick them up. Some time later Hermes returned with Poppy, accompanied by Hades, who was holding the girl tightly by the hand. When she saw her mother, Poppy broke loose and ran to kiss and hug her.

Then, seeing Zeus, she presented him with her little gift of herbs. 'I'm glad to find you at last, father,' she said.

Zeus was amazed and delighted.
First Pollo and Artemis, and now a
reunion with his long lost daughter!
'After so long!' he exclaimed.

And Demeter said to Poppy, 'You must never go
away again without telling me – in future you
must stay safely at home with your mother!'

But...

'Not possible,' said Hades. Stepping between mother and daughter, he said, 'Poppy is working for me now. She has signed a contract as my employee in the ice cream parlour, with special duties to promote my pomegranate range.'

Everyone stared at Poppy, who had turned a bright shade of pink.

'Is this true?' Demeter asked her daughter, tears springing to her eyes.

Poppy nodded. 'I do like pomegranate,' she said.

'She gets a good salary, and I've made her my hostess in the 'Underworld',' said Hades.

There was a great uproar at that, and poor Poppy looked ashamed. Zeus called for silence. 'How long is the contract for?' he asked Hades.

'For the winter months, when all my other staff are on leave,' said Hades.

Zeus, who was the head of the family and the only one who could tell Hades what to do, had to make a decision.

'In that case,' he said, 'I suggest that Poppy stays with Hades for the winter months. Then she can return to her mother in the spring and stay with her until the end of autumn. This way she will live for four months with Hades and eight months with Demeter.'

To Poppy it seemed like a tremendous idea.
Although she would not see her mother for
the four months of winter and would be
working for her uncle in the 'Underworld', she
could look forward to the spring, when not only
would the trees and plants and crops be renewed,
but her own life would be renewed as well.

The reunited family flew down from the top of the mountain in Hermes' helicopter.

In the village they were surprised to find all the other characters whom Poppy and Pollo had met on their journey waiting for them:

Poseidon, Hera, Athena, Hephaistos, Aphrodite, Ares and Dionysos!

They were all related to one another, just like
the gods and goddesses of Greek mythology,
all of which made sense because…

… they were immortal!

The Greek Gods

Zeus The king of the gods was the ruler of Mount Olympos and god of the sky, weather, thunder, lightning, law, order and justice. He carried a royal sceptre and lightning bolts, the latter thrown from on high to subdue his enemies. He had many wives, most famously Demeter and Hera, and like them many of his children were gods. His brothers, also powerful gods, were Poseidon and Hades. Roman name: Jupiter, or Jove.

Poseidon The brother of Zeus was the king of the sea, rivers, floods, droughts and earthquakes. He carried a trident, the three-pronged spear that he used on his prey and to command the elements. Roman name: Neptune.

Hades The brother of Zeus and king of the underworld and the dead. Among his many symbols was the drinking horn or *cornucopia*, and he was accompanied by his three-headed dog Cerberus. He took Persephone, the daughter of Demeter, as his consort in the underworld. Roman name: Pluto.

Hera The queen of the gods. Also goddess of empires, marriage, women and childbirth. She was both the wife and sister of Zeus and was furiously jealous of the god's other wives. She wore a diadem and veil and carried a staff with a lotus. Roman name: Juno.

Demeter The goddess of grain, agriculture, harvest and fertility. Like Hera she was both the wife and sister of Zeus and was also the mother of Persephone. She carried a torch and sheaves of wheat to symbolise the passing seasons. Roman name: Ceres.

Apollo The god of many attributes, including music, sunlight, art, poetry and archery. He was the son of Zeus and Leto, and the twin brother of Artemis. He was beardless, with long hair and manly beauty. He wore a laurel wreath and carried a lyre, a musical instrument which he played divinely. Roman name: Apollo.

Artemis Goddess of the hunt, wilderness, animals and young girls, Artemis was the daughter of Zeus and Leto, and twin sister to Apollo. She was an expert with the bow and arrow and was a great huntress, living in the universe of wild animals, notably deer, bears and wild boars. Roman name: Diana.

Hermes God of travel and communication, Hermes was also the messenger god, whose main task was to lead the souls of the dead into the afterlife. He was the son of Zeus and Maia. He carried a special herald's wand, the *caduceus*, and wore winged sandals and cap. Roman name: Mercury.

Ares The god of war was the son of Zeus and Hera, and was forever caught up in the turmoil of war, armed with spear and shield. Roman name: Mars.

Athena Goddess of wisdom and military strategy, Athena had an unusual birth, springing fully armed from the head of Zeus. She wore a crested helm and an aegis (goatskin shield) over her robe, and carried a shield and spear. She was patron of the city of Athens and her statue stood in the most sacred part of the Parthenon temple on the Acropolis. Her important symbols were the olive tree which she dedicated to the city, and the sacred owl, representing wisdom. Roman name: Minerva.

Hephaistos God of fire, metalworking and crafts. The son of Zeus and Hera, he was lame in one leg and often rode a donkey. He was the gods' blacksmith, forever working with hammer and tongs at his anvil. His most famous creation was the armour of the Greek hero Achilles. Roman name: Vulcan.

Aphrodite Goddess of beauty, love and desire. Daughter of Zeus (or the sky god Uranus) and born from the sea foam, Aphrodite had many lovers, including Adonis, Ares and Hephaistos. Recognised by her myrtle wreath and the scallop shell which carried her ashore from the waves. Roman name: Venus.

Dionysos Son of Zeus and Semele and god of wine and fruitfulness, festivals and parties, Dionysos enjoyed drunken orgies with his followers, the satyrs and maenads. He wore a crown of ivy and carried a pineapple-topped staff, the *thyrsus*, a grape vine, and a drinking cup. Roman name: Bacchus.

Persephone Daughter of Zeus and goddess of spring and vegetation through her association with her mother Demeter. She was also goddess of the underworld through her match with Hades, and the heroine of one of the greatest tales of Greek mythology. She will forever be identified with the pomegranate, whose seeds she consumed in the underworld. Her other Greek name is Kore ('maiden'). Roman name: Proserpina.